E.P.L.

Khaled and Aida

D1094600

Librairie du Liban

Among the peoples who ruled the vast wildernesses of the Sahara desert, there was once a great tribe famed for its power and wealth, and for the fierceness of its warriors in battle. The chief of this tribe was a man called Moharib, who ruled with justice and strength, caring for the needy in their distress and welcoming strangers openly and with respect.

He was helped by his minister, Zahir. Zahir was Moharib's cousin, but the two men were as brothers to each other, so close was their friendship and understanding.

Despite this, however, one day a fierce and violent quarrel broke out between the two men. The quarrel remained unsettled and, seeing that no solution was in sight, Zahir gave way to his chief and returned to his tent.

With his head hung low at this sorry turn of events, Zahir discussed the matter with his wife and together they decided that the only honourable course of action was to leave Moharib's camp and settle with the neighbouring Saad tribe.

'I would not tolerate this of any other man,' said Zahir bitterly, 'but I cannot raise my hand against one who has been a brother to me and who is chief of my tribe.'

'Leave him with the emptiness of his argument,' said his wife. 'Honour offers no other way.'

So the very next day Zahir and his wife, and all the various members of their family, took down their tents and loaded all that they possessed on to their camels, mules and horses. Then they gathered their herds of goats and sheep and set forth across the desert to the camp of the Saad tribe.

Their parting was the cause of much sorrow and regret for Moharib and Zahir, but Zahir's family were warmly welcomed by the Saad tribe and were quickly made to feel at home with them.

Zahir and his family prospered. Before long, furthermore, to the joy of all the family, Zahir's wife announced that she was expecting a baby, her first child.

It was at this time that Zahir learnt that the wife of Moharib had just had a baby son and that there was much rejoicing in Moharib's camp, for now the chief of the tribe had an heir.

When Zahir told this news to his wife he said, 'Our child is a blessing from Allah, whether it is a girl or a boy. But if it is a girl, let us pretend to everyone that it is a boy, for otherwise Moharib will gloat shamelessly in the knowledge that he has a son and heir while we still await one. I would not like to give him that pleasure.'

And indeed Zahir's first child was a girl. Zahir and his wife called the girl Aida, but to everyone else they said that they had had a baby boy whom they were going to call Djonder.

This news spread quickly throughout the camp of the Saad tribe and people came from far and wide to congratulate Zahir and his wife on the birth of their son. Zahir entertained these people lavishly and there were celebrations for several days.

Only in her tent was Aida a little girl. Outside she was the boy Djonder, trained by Zahir and other men of the tribe in the skills of horseback-riding, hunting and sword-fighting.

And there was nothing in this training, nor in the way that Aida learnt from it, to suggest that she was not a brave and gifted boy. For her father did not shrink from setting her the hardest and most dangerous challenges, each of which she faced with courage and determination so that, even as a child, she became one of the most admired and respected young fighters of her tribe, famed especially for her fearlessness in lion-hunts.

When Aida was older, Zahir gave her a place among the ranks of the warriors in the tribe. Seated on a fiery stallion and wearing a suit of armour of leather and steel, her long black hair and delicate features disguised beneath the visor of her helmet, she went to war alongside men of the tribe of her own age and fought as bravely as any of them. Indeed, before long, she showed that she was one of the tribe's most skilful warriors.

In battle she would fill the hearts of their enemies with dread as she charged forth, sword in hand, shouting 'I am Djonder, son of Zahir, unconquered horseman of the desert clans!'

All the while, at no great distance from Zahir and his daughter Aida, Moharib was bringing up his son to be a warrior of equal distinction.

The name of this boy was Khaled: he was strong, fine-looking and intelligent, in every way the worthy heir of his father. Khaled was a skilled and proud fighter, the unrivalled champion among warriors of his age; and nothing pleased him more than to test his skills to the full in combat or hunting.

As Khaled became a young man, his father Moharib became old and ill and but a few short years passed before he died. So Khaled in his turn became chief of the tribe, respected and admired by all his people.

Now, Khaled had heard much about the prowess of his cousin Djonder, son of Zahir, and had always been curious to meet him and to test his own skills against him in sporting combat — for it was said that Djonder alone possessed the exceptional skills to match his own. But Khaled's father had harboured such bitterness towards Zahir that Khaled had not been able to meet Djonder whilst his father remained alive.

Now, however, Khaled felt free to pay a visit to Zahir and his cousin Djonder. In the company of his mother and a small band of servants and warriors, he set off across the desert and rode to the camp of the Saad tribe.

There he was greeted with all honour by Zahir and entertained in magnificent style. Over the several days that Khaled stayed with Zahir's family there was an unending series of feasts and celebrations and, in respect of Khaled's famed skills as a fighter, Zahir organised a number of contests and tournaments for horsemen and warriors.

It was at such a tournament that Khaled first encountered
Aida, who, having just taken part in a contest, was still wearing
her helmet and visor, and a full set of armour.

Khaled greeted her warmly. 'My cousin Djonder,' he said,
'for too long I have been waiting for the opportunity to meet
you.' They talked for a moment before Aida excused herself,
saying that she had to return to her tent to change.

Brief though this first meeting was, Khaled felt an unusual
warmth towards his cousin – no doubt, he thought, because
they had so much in common as skilled warriors and hunters.

As for Aida, this first meeting affected her even more
deeply: she had fallen suddenly in love.

So Aida returned to her tent, bemused by this sudden heady feeling of joy. She barely slept that night, and in the morning she went to her mother and said, 'Oh mother, if Khaled leaves our camp without taking me with him as his wife, I shall die of grief.'

Now Aida's mother was delighted to hear this, for there could be no better husband for her daughter if Khaled would consent to marriage. So she said, 'Aida, my dear, you must be patient for a little while. Do not reveal your love for Khaled quite yet, but rather let me talk to his mother later today. I will be able to explain the whole story to her, and I am sure that, through her, we will be able to arrange your marriage to Khaled. Nothing would bring greater happiness to me or your father.'

So Zahir's wife awaited the right opportunity to talk to Khaled's mother in confidence, and when such a moment arose, she spoke frankly and at length. Then she called for Aida and said, 'This is my daughter Aida, who for all her youthful years has played the part of Djonder on the battlefield and in the hunting grounds.'

Khaled's mother was stunned into silence for a moment. 'Let me look at you,' she said softly to Aida at last. Aida stepped forward.

'Well!' exclaimed Khaled's mother. 'Among all the women of the Arab lands never have I seen greater beauty than this. Aida, you are a rare pearl. I cannot imagine there can be anyone who might bring greater happiness to my son.'

So Khaled's mother went to her son and explained the story of Djonder and Aida to him. He sat in amazement at the news that such a feared and respected champion as Djonder should in fact be a woman.

'But this is the truth,' his mother insisted. 'And the truth is yet more extraordinary. For Aida is a woman of unrivalled beauty, a moon among the stars. Now, I know you do not have to listen to the advice of your ageing mother, but of this I am quite certain: if you go to your cousin Zahir and ask him for his daughter's hand in marriage, your request will be gladly honoured. And to have Aida as your wife will bring you all the happiness you could wish for.'

Khaled sat in silence for a while, his brow knitted in troubled thought. Then at last he said, 'Let us leave this camp today. I am not at all happy with this turn of events: whatever you might say about Aida – rare beauty that she may be – she has had too strange a childhood to make her suited to be my wife. At one moment a warrior of manly courage, now a girl suddenly in love: this hardly shows the kind of background or temperament I would expect of the wife of a chief, who must be able to command the respect of his tribe. Far from what you think, mother, this is not the kind of woman I wish to marry.'

And with this Khaled mounted his horse and, bidding his cousin Zahir a brief farewell, hastily rode away from the camp of the Saad tribe, leaving his servants and warriors to dismantle their tents and to follow in his tracks in the company of his mother.

This sudden departure came as a shock to Zahir and his family, and in particular to Aida, who felt that Khaled had intended to insult her.

Her feelings of both love and anger distressed her almost to illness, so much so that, when her father gathered a band of warriors to attack a neighbouring enemy, he did not insist that she joined them. Rather, he thought, she should be allowed to recover in her own time.

As soon as her father and the warriors had left, however, Aida put on a suit of black armour and a black helmet, mounted her stallion, and rode like the south wind across the scorched landscape to the place where Khaled's tribe had camped.

In the disguise of her armour, with the visor of her helmet covering her face, Aida went through the camp to the place where strangers were welcomed and lodged. Here she was given a tent of her own, where she lay down to rest.

The next day a series of tournaments began, with warriors and horsemen challenging each other to contests with spears and lances, swords, knives and axes.

It was a day marked by a stunning display of fighting skills: many of the greatest fighters of the land had gathered here and the contests were long and hard. But the unquestioned champion was an unknown stranger who won the respect and admiration of all: Aida.

Khaled looked on, knowing that on the following day he must demonstrate his own skills against this champion.

In the pink light of the early hours the following morning, Khaled put on his armour at the edge of the field of combat, eyeing his opponent, the unknown stranger.

Their contest began slowly, each trying to discover the other's weaknesses, each testing the other's skills – quickness in attack, alertness in defence.

And then the fight began in earnest: the slashing of steel; the deadening reports of steel against the thick leather shields; quick, agile steps kicking up clouds of stifling dust.

They tested each other to the limits of their skills and endurance but neither could find any advantage over the other, until at last, by sheer strength, Khaled knocked Aida to the ground with a blow of his sword and could have finished the contest there and then.

But in honour of his opponent, Khaled withdrew: the contest, he said, was to be declared a draw.

The next day, as he saw this stranger about to depart on horseback, he called out, 'Good sir, my most worthy opponent. Courtesy forbids me from asking who you are and where you come from. But curiosity burns within me.'

'Khaled,' replied his opponent, 'you know me already. I am your cousin Aida. Do you remember – the woman whose love you so promptly rejected? Farewell!'

And with this she spurred her horse forth, out of the camp and into the heat of the desert.

Khaled returned to his tent, his head dizzy in the confusion of feelings which he now experienced. For it was beginning to be clear to him that a deep love for Aida had been quietly growing inside him.

Troubled by this, Khaled spoke to his mother and poured out his grief to her.

'Be patient,' she said. 'I will talk to Aida's mother and I am sure that, before long, we will secure a happy outcome.'

So Khaled's mother, in the company of a group of servants and warriors, crossed the desert, following in the tracks of Aida.

When Khaled's mother reached the camp of the Saad tribe, she was warmly greeted by Zahir's wife. Before long she came to explain the purpose of her visit, and pleaded with Zahir's wife to allow their daughter to marry Khaled.

But Zahir's wife could only ask Khaled's mother to await the return of Zahir, who was still away waging a campaign against his enemies. 'However,' she added, 'I will speak to Aida: I am sure she will be delighted with the news of Khaled's offer of marriage.'

To their surprise, however, Aida was far from pleased. 'I fought Khaled only to abate my rage at his refusal of me,' she replied. 'Now my pride prevents me from accepting his hand in marriage.'

Khaled's mother returned to her own tribe bearing this disappointing news. Khaled was alarmed and upset, while Aida's refusal of him only increased his determination to marry her. Once again, he turned to his mother for advice.

'I see there is only one thing you might do,' said his mother. 'Wait until your cousin Zahir returns from his campaign and then assemble a company of your greatest warriors and the chiefs of the tribes who are your allies. Then go with these men to Zahir's tents and plead with him for the hand of his daughter in marriage. He will say that he has but a son, Djonder, so you must tell him that you know the truth. In such company he will understand the seriousness of your request.'

So on Zahir's return Khaled called together his warriors and the neighbouring chiefs and told them of this plan. Although they were astonished to hear that Zahir's famous son was in fact a woman, they agreed to help Khaled in his quest.

So the chiefs of the tribes and their greatest warriors assembled in their finery and, in the company of Khaled and a caravan of pack-animals bearing splendid gifts, they marched towards the camp of the Saad tribe. There they were greeted with great ceremony by Zahir, who believed that they had come to welcome him home from war and to congratulate him on his victories – and perhaps even to invite him and his family to return to live among the family of Moharib, as they had done in the past.

For three days Zahir entertained his guests lavishly, seeing to their every need and comfort.

On the fourth day Khaled went to Zahir and asked for his daughter's hand in marriage.

24

'You know that I have no daughter,' said Zahir, confused by this request, 'only my son, Djonder.'

But Khaled told him how he had come to know about Aida, how first she had fallen in love with him, and now he with her, and how they had fought, and how he now pressed for her hand in marriage.

'So my secret has been revealed,' said Zahir. 'It shames me to be reminded of what I have done to conceal my daughter from my brother Moharib's tribe. Yet if the outcome is that my daughter should marry the son of Moharib, I could not hope for a happier conclusion. Yes, I consent; she shall be your wife.'

Now, when Aida heard that she was to be married to Khaled she quickly swallowed her resentment, for this was her father's instruction and, furthermore, if she was to marry at all, Khaled might be as acceptable as any man.

'But,' Aida said to her father, 'if he is to make me a happy bride he must first prove his worth. To the west our old enemies threaten our pastures and prosperity once more. Let Khaled go out and defeat them once and for all, and when he returns victorious I shall marry him gladly.'

When Khaled heard of the task that Aida demanded of him, he accepted without hesitation.

Khaled set out across the desert with his army of warriors, the sun glinting on the shining steel of their sharpened weapons and on the smooth backs of their powerful horses.

In little time he had returned, to be welcomed home by the clash of cymbals and great rejoicing. For he had won a swift and famous victory over Zahir's enemies, and he himself had outshone all the other warriors by his exceptional courage and valour.

A marriage date was set a full moon from his return. It was to be a magnificent event, with guests from all over the land. Khaled was overjoyed – and near to bursting with pride and self-esteem.

Now, Aida saw the extent of Khaled's self-esteem and was frightened by it: for had it not been just such vanity that had caused him once to spurn her love?

So she said, 'The guests for our marriage are coming from all parts of this land, yet we have heard that hungry lions stalk the desert, causing numerous deaths of innocent travellers in recent months. Should it not be Khaled's duty to clear the land of these lions before our guests make their way to us?'

When Khaled heard this suggestion he was delighted, for nothing pleased him more than to go out hunting. He gathered together the most skilled hunters from among his men, saddled a team of horses, and set off into the wilderness.

As soon as Khaled had left the camp, Aida disguised herself as a camel-driver, with a flowing robe, a turban, and a dust-mask over her face. Then she saddled a horse and raced across the desert towards the hills, leaving a trail of billowing dust behind her.

In the hills she sought out a cavern where two man-eating lionesses were known to lurk. Approaching the cavern on foot, she heard the angry growls of the beasts as they crouched on ledges above her, ready to pounce.

Suddenly the two lionesses threw themselves at her, flying through the air with a horrifying roar. But Aida stepped back deftly and, awaiting her moment with a knife in one hand and her sword in the other, swiftly and skilfully killed each lioness in turn.

Then she went into the cavern to await Khaled's arrival.

It was not long before Khaled and his hunting party came
within sight of the cavern. They were surprised to see the two
dead lionesses stretched out on the ground before them, and
even more surprised to be addressed by the angry voice of a
stranger from the mouth of the cavern, hailing Khaled with
these words: 'Throw down your sword and walk away from
here, if you value your life.'

Khaled dismounted to confront this challenge, saying,
'Stranger, reconsider! You do not know who I am and that my
name spells death to the unruly.'

And then the two crossed swords and furious battle
ensued.

Long and hard they fought in the searing heat of the day. In the eyes of his opponent Khaled saw a glint of fearsome determination that alarmed him, and he had to repulse a series of attacks of furious pitch such as he had never before encountered.

At last, seeing that he could not score a victory without risking everything, he stood back and called a halt to the fray.

'Stranger,' he said, panting heavily, 'nothing more can come of this. Let us call this fight a draw and go our separate ways. But please at least let me know with whom I have had the honour of this combat.'

Aida removed her dust-mask. 'Let this be the final lesson about your pride and mine, Khaled,' she said coolly. 'It has taken this to prove that the girl that you love can be your equal, without which I could not marry you.'

Together they rode back to the camp, matching each other stride for stride on their powerful horses, with the pounding of the hooves and the whistling wind ringing in their ears.

As they approached the camp they could see the smoke rising from fires that had been lit to prepare food for the wedding feast, and trails of people coming across the desert from all directions to the joyous sound of drums and cymbals.